D0102303

The Perfect Pet

Written by Russell Punter

Illustrated by Mike and Carl Gordon

How this book works

The story of **The Perfect Pet** has been written for you to read with your child. You take turns to read:

You read these words.

Your child reads these words.

You don't have to finish the story in one session. If your child is getting tired, put a marker in the page and come back to it later.

You can find out more about helping your child with this book, and with reading in general, on pages 30-31.

The Perfect Pet

Turn the page to start the story.

Nell doesn't care for shopping.
"Dad! Are we finished yet?"
She sees a store that looks more fun.

Can I go in
and pick a pet?

5

Here's Tess and Ted.
They're glad to help,
with pets both small and big.

"A dog is
a lot of fun."

"A pup can
beg and dig."

Dad's not so sure.
"Dogs make a mess.
And who would clean it up?"
Nell begs and pleads,
     but Dad won't budge.

9

"Well, how about a snake?" says Ted.
"Sid's very friendly, miss."
Sid ties himself around Dad's neck.

A parrot snatches at Dad's cap,
And perches on a rack.
"No need to worry, sir," says Tess.

Dad helps Ted chase the parrot.
They just can't jump high enough.
Ted tries to catch it in a net.

Dad and Ted
huff and puff.

Nell sees a bat hang upside down.
It looks so very still,
Dad thinks there's something
    wrong with it.

"He's only sleeping, sir," says Tess.
"Bats do a lot of that."
"I think he's really cute," says Nell.

Nell counts out all her money, but –
"That's not enough," says Tess.
Then Ted finds something cheaper.
"Look!"

"Is this the pet you want?" asks Dad.
Nell nods and smiles, "You bet!
That was the greatest shopping trip."

"I had fun
and I got a pet."

Puzzle 1

Match the words to the pictures on the opposite page.

1. **Pat him.
Let him hiss.**

2. **A pup can
beg and dig.**

3. **A bug on
a log is less.**

4. **Dad, can I
get a bat?**

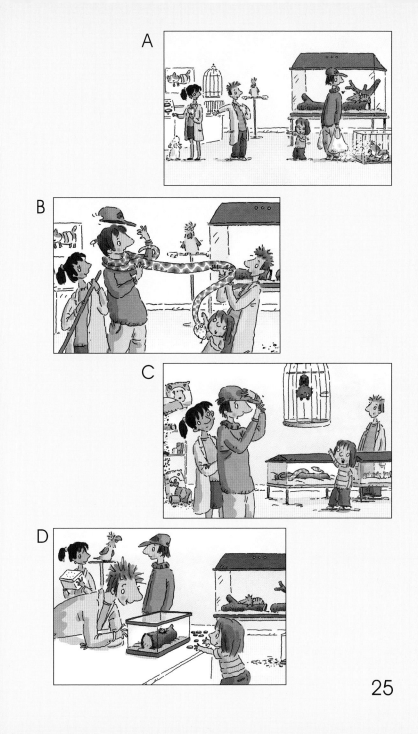

25

Puzzle 2

There is one wrong word in the sentence below each picture. What should it say?

1.

Can I go in and pick a pat?

2.

Ted can bet it back.

3.

Tess, sell us, is it ill?

4.

I had bun
and I got a pet.

Puzzle 3

Look at the picture, then read the words below. Which five things are in the picture?

- a dog   - a cap
- a doll   - a log
- a pig   - a fan
- a hen   - a bat
- a bag   - a bed

Answers to puzzles

Puzzle 1
1. Pat him. Let him hiss. – B
2. A pup can beg and dig. – A
3. A bug on a log is less. – D
4. Dad, can I get a bat? – C

Puzzle 2
1. Can I go in and pick a ~~pet~~?
   Can I go in and pick a pet?
2. Ted can ~~bet~~ it back.
   Ted can get it back.
3. Tess, ~~sell~~ us, is it ill?
   Tess, tell us, is it ill?
4. I had ~~bun~~, and I got a pet.
   I had fun, and I got a pet.

Puzzle 3

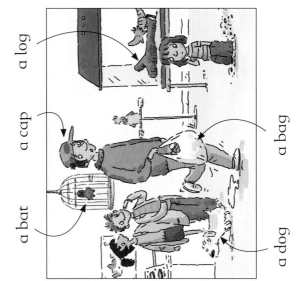

a bat   a cap   a log

a dog   a bag

Guidance notes

Usborne Very First Reading is a series of books, specially developed for children who are learning to read. In the early books in the series, you and your child take turns to read, and your child steadily builds the knowledge and confidence to read alone.

The words for your child to read in **The Perfect Pet** introduce these seven letters or letter-combinations:

h	b	f	ff	l	ll	ss

Your child will soon grasp that **ff** has the same sound as **f**, **ll** as **l** and **ss** as **s**. These are often among the first letters that children learn to read at school. Later books in the series gradually introduce more letters, sounds and spelling patterns, while reinforcing the ones your child already knows.

You'll find lots more information about the structure of the series, advice on helping your child with reading, extra practice activities and games on the Very First Reading website,* **www.usborne.com/veryfirstreading**

*US readers go to **www.veryfirstreading.com**

Some questions and answers

- **Why do I need to read with my child?**
  Sharing stories and taking turns makes reading an enjoyable and fun activity for children. It also helps them to develop confidence and reading stamina, and to take part in an exciting story using very few words.

- **When is a good time to read?**
  Choose a time when you are both relaxed, but not too tired, and there are no distractions. Only read for as long as your child wants to – you can always try again another day.

- **What if my child gets stuck?**
  Don't simply read the problem word yourself, but prompt your child and try to find the right answer together. Similarly, if your child makes a mistake, go back and look at the word together. Don't forget to give plenty of praise and encouragement.

- **We've finished, now what do we do?**
  It's a good idea to read the story several times to give your child more practice and confidence. Then you can try reading **A Bus for Miss Moss** at the same level or, when your child is ready, go on to Book 4 in the series.

Edited by Jenny Tyler, Lesley Sims
and Mairi Mackinnon

First published in 2011 by Usborne Publishing Ltd., Usborne House,
83-85 Saffron Hill, London EC1N 8RT, England. www.usborne.com
Copyright © 2011 Usborne Publishing Ltd.